C000221082

Other Titles of Interest

MAGIC ELECTRONIC PROJECTS

by

ROY BEBBINGTON, MISTC

BERNARD BABANI (publishing) LTD
THE GRAMPIANS
SHEPHERDS BUSH ROAD
LONDON W6 7NF
ENGLAND

Please Note

Although every care has been taken with the production of this book to ensure that any projects, designs, modifications and/or programs, etc., contained herewith, operate in a correct and safe manner and also that all components specified are normally available in Great Britain, the Publishers and Author do not accept responsibility in any way for the failure, including fault in design, of any project, design, modification or program to work correctly or to cause damage to any other equipment that it may be connected to or used in conjunction with, or in respect of any other damage or injury that may be so caused, nor do the Publishers accept responsibility in any way for the failure to obtain specified components.

Notice is also given that if equipment that is still under warranty is modified in any way or used or connected with home-built equipment then that warranty may be void.

© 1993 BERNARD BABANI (publishing) LTD

First Published — July 1993

British Library Cataloguing in Publication Data
Bebbington, R.
    Magic Electronic Projects
    I. Title
    621.381

    ISBN 0 85934 334 0

Printed and Bound in Great Britain by Cox & Wyman Ltd, Reading

Preface

"Technology is almost magical!"

— President Bill Clinton

A book of magic tricks with a difference — magic elec-tricks!
Over thirty worked-out magic tricks with an electronic flavour
and suggestions for others. Conjure up lights, sounds, movement that puzzle and entertain your friends.

You too can be a member of the Magic Circle if you play
your cards right!

Let's face it, electrics and electronics should be prime
subjects for magic tricks — in this pushbutton age most everyday electronic gadgets seem to be magic. But ask yourself how
many books have you seen on electronic magic? Having
decided on electronic magic as the theme for a book, I visited
the local library where 'Abracadabra', it appeared as if by
magic, that all the books on this subject had mysteriously
vanished into thin air. There were books on magic, and
books on electronics, but never the twain seemed to meet.
I suspect there are some, but not a lot!

The problem is that electronic wizardry has become so
commonplace that it is universally accepted without even a
raised eyebrow. Light at the flick of a switch, distant sounds
from a radio and pictures on a TV screen wouldn't even raise
a 'Hey Presto!' any more. They may still be mysteries to
many, but, like the magic lantern, they are no longer magic
— they are now the expected. For electronic tricks to be
effective the magician needs to pull the unexpected out of
the hat: light without switches, a wireless that is truly
wire-less, circuits with deductive powers, mysterious movement of objects without cause — apparently!

Elaborate stage props are often frowned upon by the 'real'
magician who prefers close-up magic and sleight of hand
tricks. Here are some tricks for those interested in magic and
electronics, including simple pieces of apparatus that will produce or enhance your magical effects — sometimes using
sleight of hand or more aptly in other cases, light of hand!

Roy Bebbington

Contents

Introduction

What do we mean by magic?

In our case, 'light-hearted deception for the sake of entertainment — sounds and lights out of thin air, things that go bump in the night'. Magic is a visual art, the entertainment value being limited only by the performer's and spectator's imagination. To a child at a party, magic is a whole new world of wonder — it's fun!

Presentation

The enjoyment of magic is the mystery of how it happens, so don't break the spell by telling how a trick is done, and don't go in for repeats. Practice makes perfect, so rehearse your tricks in front of a mirror until you are sure that what the audience sees is what you want it to see.

Use misdirection to distract audience attention from the tricky part. Remember, you are supposed to be a magician, so act the part! Relax and be casual, especially when you are attempting a sleight of hand. Any tenseness at the critical moment will surely signpost the very thing you don't want to be signposted.

Work out a routine from the tricks you choose — these should be the ones you do best. Make your first trick direct, but build it up carefully so that it's not all over before your onlookers realise it. Give them something spectacular that obviously marks the end of the trick. Try to link your programme so that one trick follows on naturally from the one before. During tricks that require some skill, throw in one or two that are straightforward. You will find that the audience will give you more credit for them than they deserve.

Props

Make the props colourful and attractive. Even a simple trick can be made more effective by interesting equipment and a good line of patter. Many of the electrical tricks based on deception use a sensor to produce or control light, sound and movement. Typical sensors are: light-dependent resistors, reed switches, manual switches, touch switches, gravity switches, microphones, etc. Some of these are used in the following tricks. From these sensors, simple circuits can produce some spectacular or unexplainable light, sound or movement effects. Although not used in this book, infra-red transmissions could also be used to trigger some effects.

The most usual effects in magic can be categorised as: vanishing and appearing tricks, changes, penetrating solids, mind-reading, predicting. You can concentrate on some of these effects in a programme selected from the following tricks. These will no doubt suggest to you more electrical and electronic circuits that can be used to produce other tricks.

Even if you don't fancy performing your electronic magic in front of an audience, you can still try out some of these tricks on your friends.

Chapter 1

LED ASTRAY

Light-emitting diodes (LEDs) provide the visual effects in this first group of tricks. For indicator circuits, the advantages over filament lamps are that LEDs draw only a few milliamps and are low-voltage devices. A voltage-limiting series resistor is needed if voltages above 2V are used. Light-emitting diodes need to be connected the right way round, i.e. anode to the positive supply voltage, cathode to the negative supply voltage. Usually, there is a flat on the body against the cathode connection, and the cathode lead is shorter than the anode lead. However, correct polarity can easily be checked by connecting the LED in series with a $1k\Omega$ resistor and a 9V battery.

The cathode of the tri-colour LED, used later in this chapter, is the middle lead of the three. The flat on the body is adjacent to the red anode connection.

1. Magic Bracelet
A number of separate LEDs are placed in a paper cup together with a length of connecting wire and a small battery. The cup is covered with an empty cardboard tube while a wand (or soldering iron) is waved and a few choice words are spoken. When the cup is removed, the LEDs are tipped out, strung together in a glowing bracelet, as if by magic.

Preparation
This trick requires two sets of identical components, one set made up into a complete bracelet as shown in Figure 1.1. A series string of four LEDs is connected across a 9V battery (PP3). A two-string bracelet looks more spectacular if you are feeling extravagent.

Two large paper cups are needed, and a slightly larger cardboard tube to hide these cups when one cup is fitted inside the other.

The inner cup must be suitably prepared. Remove the bottom and glue a false bottom about an inch higher up to make a space between the cups for loading the bracelet. Make

3

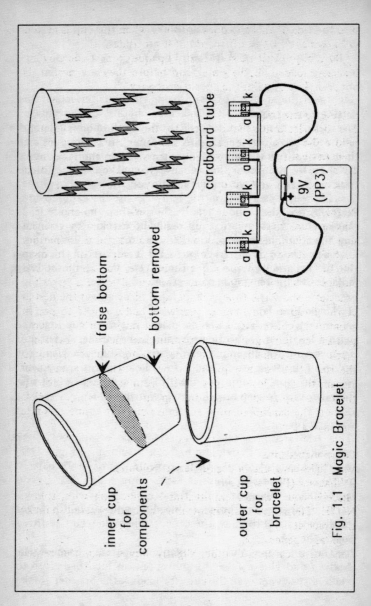

cardboard tube

false bottom

bottom removed

inner cup for components

outer cup for bracelet

Fig. 1.1 Magic Bracelet

k a k a k a k a

9V (PP3)

sure the rim of this cup does not show when this cup is nested in the other cup. Cut off the rim if it protrudes.

Both cups must be sufficiently opaque so that the glowing bracelet, loaded in the outer cup before they are nested, is not seen; line or paint the cups if necessary.

Setting up the trick

The bracelet must be clipped to the battery immediately before the trick and loaded into the outer cup. The cups are then nested and the loose components put in the inner cup. To conserve the battery, you can either make this your first trick or get an assistant to set it up for you.

Performance

Making sure that nested cups remain together, tip out the separate components on to your close-up mat for examination. Give the cup a shake to indicate that it is empty. As you drop the LEDs back into the cup one by one, you could tell the audience that, wired together, they would make a sparkling bracelet. Show the tube is empty and place it over the nested cups. 'Drop in some connecting wire, and we need to pop in a battery,' you could add. 'Soldering might be a problem,' you say as you wave a soldering iron over the tube. Say some magic words and lift up the tube, making sure you also grip the rim of the inner cup as you do so. The outer cup will remain on the close-up mat. With your other hand, lift up the outer cup from the mat and tip out the glowing bracelet. Discard the cardboard tube and inner cup. It's time to smile and take a bow!

Components List

Four light-emitting diodes (different colours).
9V battery (PP3) with clip.
Miscellaneous: flexible multi-strand connecting wire, solder.
NOTE: The above components must all be duplicated to make the bracelet.
Two large paper cups.
Decorative cardboard tube, slightly longer than the nested cups.

2. Hanky Panky

Display a clean white handkerchief and spread it on a table. Invite someone to examine a stray LED and place it in the centre of the handkerchief. Fold it in the handkerchief, wave the magic wand, speak the magic word' and the LED will mysteriously appear to light up. Shake the handkerchief, the light will go out, and your stray LED will fall to the table. Wave the handkerchief and show both sides before pocketing it.

Method

The secret of this trick is the LED circuit wired into the hem of the handkerchief (see Figure 1.2). This can be powered by

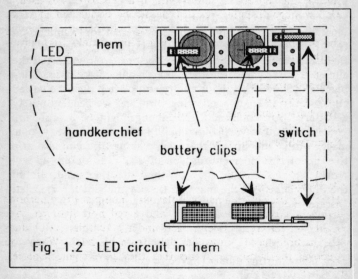

Fig. 1.2 LED circuit in hem

two mercuric oxide button batteries in series. These batteries give 1.35V each, so two are necessary to provide the 2V required for the LED. The HG3 type, for instance, is 7.9mm diameter by 3.5mm high and has a nominal capacity of 40mAh. Perhaps the biggest problem is to find or make a battery holder for these. Discarded musical greetings cards could be a useful source. If all else fails, battery clips can be devised from small lengths of springy contact strip of the kind used in miniature relays. These can be mounted on a small piece of printed-circuit board as shown, together with an improvised push-switch. A handkerchief with a wide hem (17mm) would in fact take AAA-size batteries, but these may need a little more dexterity to connect and hide.

An alternative power source for this trick and several others, is a glove-held battery. The contact areas can be small, inconspicuous press-studs sewn into the thumb and middle finger pads. These can make contact with two similar press-studs sewn on opposite sides of one corner of the handkerchief that complete the circuit to the LED inserted in the hem. Remember that correct polarity (LED anode to the positive side of the battery) is important. If a PP3 battery is used, a $1k\Omega$ voltage-dropping resistor should be connected in series with it. This resistor will also prevent the battery becoming short-circuit if the thumb and finger press-studs are inadvertently touched together.

Components List
Two red LEDs
Two button cells (HG3 or similar)
Battery clip and wiring
Clean, white handkerchief

3. Harbour Lights
Here is a trick with a nautical flavour. You place two harbour lights, a green starboard light and a red port light to your right and left respectively, each under a tumbler. But does the harbourmaster know his right from his left? When you uncover the lamps it appears that they have changed places.

Preparation
You need to make up two identical astable multivibrator circuits as shown in Figure 1.3. The two transistors are cross-coupled by electrolytic capacitors C1 and C2. The changing voltages as these capacitors charge up cause the on/off states of the circuit to flip backwards and forwards at a rate depending on the values of C1, R2, and C2, R3. Increase component

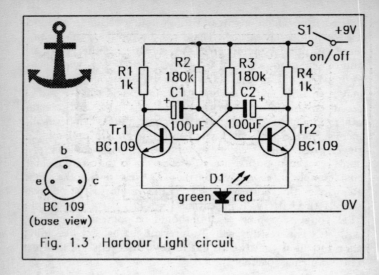

Fig. 1.3 Harbour Light circuit

values to slow down the flip-flop rate and vice versa. The values chosen cause Tr1 and Tr2 to conduct alternately for about 15 seconds each. This means that the tri-colour LED, D1 in the emitter circuits changes colour every 15 seconds, i.e. is alternately red and green.

Each circuit is built on a small piece of stripboard as shown in Figure 1.4. For this layout, it is only necessary to make two breaks in the bottom copper strip to include D1 in the emitter circuit of Tr1 and Tr2. The common cathode of D1, the centre lead, is connected to the 0V line.

The two circuits can be mounted in plastic or cardboard containers, preferably tubular. The aim should be to make them look like identical twin buoys, each with D1 mounted centrally at the top.

Presentation
Place the two harbour lights in front of you, explaining that the harbourmaster put the marker buoys one at each side of the harbour entrance to help shipping. Cover each with a tumbler as you switch them on so that the audience cannot see the lights and that they change colour. Tilt up the tumbler on

8

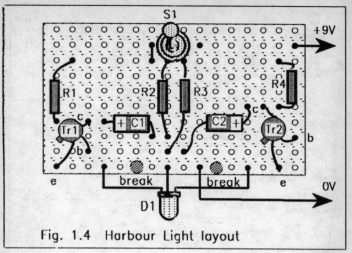

Fig. 1.4 Harbour Light layout

your right side a little way from you to take a peep at the light without the audience seeing it. Wait until it turns to green and lift up the tumbler immediately to show it, saying, 'Of course, the harbourmaster put the green light on the starboard side (right side) for ships going into harbour.' Replace the tumbler before the light changes to red. Then tilt the left-hand tumbler to peep at the light. Immediately it turns red, lift up the tumbler to show the colour and say, 'And he put the red light on the port side (left side).' Replace the tumbler before the light changes to green. By tilting the tumblers towards you, waiting and lifting you can assure your audience that the lights are where they are supposed to be, green on the right, red on the left.

'That's fine coming in, said one of the skippers, but what about coming out of harbour. Won't we see a red light on the starboard side and a green light on the port side?'

Point to your right-hand tumbler and say, 'You mean this should be red?' Tilt, wait and lift it up to reveal a red light for a few seconds. Now point to the left-hand tumbler and say, 'and this should be green?' Tilt, wait and lift to reveal a green light. Replace the tumbler and take a bow.

Components List per light circuit

Resistors

R1	1kΩ
R2	180kΩ
R3	180kΩ
R4	1kΩ

Capacitors

C1	100μF
C2	100μF

Semiconductors

Tr1	BC109
Tr2	BC109
D1	Tri-colour LED

Switch

S1	S.P.S.T. on/off

Miscellaneous

9V-battery (PP3) and clip, stripboard, connecting wire, suitable container to house circuit, large tumbler (opaque).

4. Port/Starboard

Here is another nautical trick that needs dressing up with a story as you perform it. Try something like this.

To a sailor, the port side of a ship is the left-hand side, and the starboard side is the right-hand side — that's when standing on deck, looking towards the sharp end. And, as we see on the SS Redgreen, for ships that pass in the night the port side is indicated by a red lamp, and the starboard side by a green lamp. Sea lanes are very wide, and to avoid collisions there's a rule of the road that goes, 'Green to green and red to red, perfect safety, go ahead!'

But the captain of the SS Tricolor was too mean to fit two lights. He said he could manage with only one light on the mast — and a white light at that! 'White? Oh no it's not,' he said switching it on (the lamp will glow either red or green). 'Won't that be confusing,' you ask? 'Not all all! This lamp has extraordinary powers of observation; if a ship passes on the port side, (demonstrate) it glows red, and if it passes on the starboard side it glows green. As you see, it obeys the rule of the road: green to green and red to red, perfect safety, go ahead!'

Preparation

You will need to obtain or make two model boat shapes about six inches long. These can be made from stout card or thin plywood and can be as simple or elaborate as you wish.

As Figure 1.5 shows, the good ship SS Redgreen conceals a strong magnet in its bows that will actuate one of the reed switches of the other ship when it passes nearby. The circuit of the SS Redgreen is simply two LEDs in parallel connected in series with a limiting resistor and switch. Red- and green-coloured imitation lamps could replace this circuit, but the two glowing LEDs add to the general effect.

Figure 1.6 shows the circuit and general layout of the SS Tricolor. Hide the two reed switches in the bows to make it less obvious how the tri-colour LED changes over.

The circuit is known as an RS (set-reset) flip-flop. At switch-on, one of the transistors Tr1 or Tr2 will conduct depending upon circuit tolerances. If, for instance, Tr1 conducts, it will be held on by the cross-over resistor, R3 connecting its base to the +9V rail via R4. In this case, Tr2 will be held off because its base will be held low via R2 by the low collector voltage on Tr1 as it conducts. Light-emitting diode D1 will glow red because of the voltage applied via R4.

Alternatively, if Tr2 conducts at switch-on, Tr1 is held off, and D1 will glow green because of the voltage applied via R1.

Whatever the colour of D1 at switch-on, e.g. green, it can be changed to the opposite colour, red in this case, by approaching the SS Redgreen on the red side.

In effect, changeover from one state to the other is made by bringing the magnet close to the reed switch (RS1 or RS2) in the base circuit of the transistor that is conducting. If the magnet is strong enough, and the reed switches well forward, both could operate in the head-on position. These short-circuit both bases to the 0V rail and switch off both transistors.

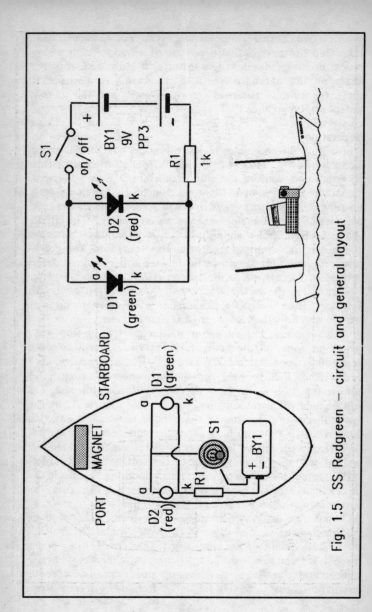

Fig. 1.5 SS Redgreen – circuit and general layout

12

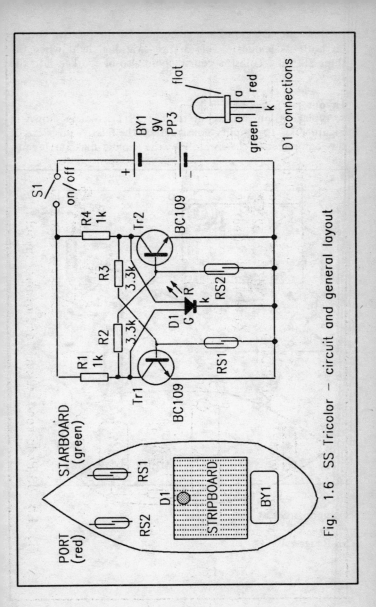

Fig. 1.6 SS Tricolor – circuit and general layout

13

In this state, D1 glows orange because of the positive voltage on both its anodes. This orange 'warning' light when the ships are on a collision course could also be worked into the story.

Layout
A typical stripboard layout for the SS Tricolor is shown in Figure 1.7. To simplify construction, the relative positions of the components closely follow the circuit diagram layout.

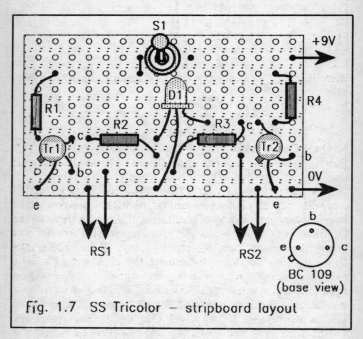

Fig. 1.7 SS Tricolor — stripboard layout

Components List

SS Redgreen

R1	1kΩ
D1	Green LED
D2	Red LED

14

S1   S.P.S.T.
Miscellaneous: PP3 battery with connector, wire.

SS Tricolor:
R1   1kΩ
R2   3.3kΩ
R3   3.3kΩ
R4   1kΩ
Tr1   BC109
Tr2   BC109
D1   Tri-colour LED
S1   S.P.S.T.
RS1   reed switch
RS2   reed switch
Miscellaneous: PP3 battery with connector, stripboard and wire.

5. Open Circuit LEDs

Here's a trick that requires some sleight of hand. It's a circuit that refuses to go open-circuit even when you cut it!

Pick up a string of four LEDs connected in series with a crocodile clip at each end. Explain that they are connected in series and obviously, they will light if you clip them to the terminals of a battery, like so! And to switch them off you break the circuit somewhere, you say, disconnecting the crocodile clips in turn. Reconnect the clips and pick up a pair of scissors or wire cutters. Of course, we can make an open-circuit anywhere, you continue, grasping a section of the cable. Bend it in one hand for all to see and then cut it. The audience will be surprised that the lamps remain on.

The trick is in the insulating sleeving between two of the LEDs. A slit has been prepared in it beforehand. As you bend the cable into a loop in your hand, pull gently on the two adjacent LEDs. The connecting wire will pass through the slit in the insulation and will be hidden by your hand. With a flourish of the scissors, you then proceed to snip through the loop of insulation and show the two cut ends to the audience. Still grasping the loop in your left hand, unclip

15

the string of LEDs and discard it to a servante, the magicians' name for a hidden pocket at the rear of your table.

Preparation
The four LEDs should be wired in series as shown in Figure 1.8, i.e. positive clip to LED1 anode, LED1 cathode to LED2 anode, LED2 cathode to LED3 anode, LED3 cathode to LED4 anode and LED4 cathode to the negative clip. Use

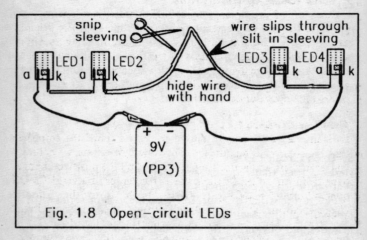

Fig. 1.8   Open–circuit LEDs

about 8-in lengths of copper wire with PVC insulating sleeving for each link. The sleeving should be slightly larger than necessary, say 3–4mm diameter, so that the wire is free to slide through the section that contains the slit. You will need to prepare and replace the split section of sleeving before your next performance.

An even more convincing open-circuit trick that needs no sleight of hand is given under Chapter 3. Light Fantastic.

Components List
4 LEDs, 9V-battery and clips, copper wire and sleeving as text.

Chapter 2

SWITCHCRAFT

Introduce a few switches in a circuit and the way it works may not be very obvious, especially if a switch is hidden.

1. Many Hands Make Light Work

I once coined the phrase, 'many lights make hands work!' to promote the use of electricity on farms, but even the original saying 'Many hands make light work', takes on a new meaning with this trick. It's switchcraft of a different kind when a light is switched as you shake hands with a spectator. And to prove you don't have a hidden switch up your sleeve, let two spectators take over the demonstration.

The Circuit (Figure 2.1)

Basically, a touch switch is used to drive a transistor amplifier that has a lamp in its output. The touch switch uses a Schmitt trigger circuit to ensure that there is a rapid, positive change-over from one state to the other. Two gates of a 4011 CMOS quad 2-input NAND gate, IC1a, IC1b, form the Schmitt trigger. Normally, the input and output of the trigger circuit are at a low logic level and consequently the transistor Tr1 is held off. A touch on the contacts with the hands supplies base current from the +6V rail via the skin resistance. The input to inverter IC1a goes high, its output goes low and so IC1b input goes low. Inverted, this gives a high on IC1b output, which provides base current to turn on Tr1 and light the lamp.

It is advisable to take the inputs of the unused gates to one of the supply rails to prevent extra power being consumed due to stray pick up.

Components List

Resistors

R1	3.9MΩ
R2	10MΩ
R3	1kΩ

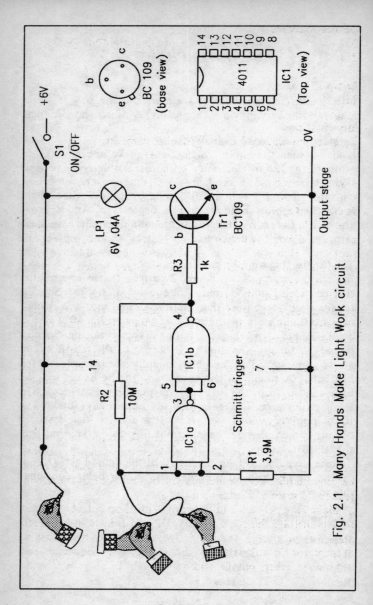

Fig. 2.1 Many Hands Make Light Work circuit

18

Semiconductors

IC1   4011 CMOS Quad 2-input NAND gate
Tr1   BC109

Lamp

LP1   6V 0.04A m.e.s. bulb

Miscellaneous

Case, stripboard, 6V battery with clip, wire, etc.

2. Traffic Lights

The traffic lights have failed, but this simple circuit consisting of three lights, switches and a battery should present no problem. However, things are not what they seem and manual operation is complicated by a hidden rotary switch when you ask one of the audience to operate them.

The main circuit can be surface-mounted on a wooden panel in heavy wiring as shown in Figure 2.2. The three LEDs, red, orange and green, are grouped like a traffic light with a painted surround to add a touch of realism. The idea is that the circuit operation should look obvious and straightforward. At the three points near D1 — D3, where the S4 switch breaks into the main circuit, the insulated wires from S1, S2 and S3 should appear to go direct to D1, D2 and D3. Three small holes in the front panel, taking the leads to S4, are hidden by the insulation.

Ideally, the hidden rotary switch S4 should be a single wafer, set into the panel so the back panel can be shown, operated by a detachable control arm. Failing this, S4 could be mounted at the rear in a shallow box and one of the rubber feet could serve as a rotary control.

Make sure that S4 is in the correct position before you start to demonstrate this trick, i.e. D1, D2 and D3 are lit by S1, S2 and S3 respectively. Then secretly give S4 a turn before asking a spectator to run through the traffic light sequence: red, red-orange, green, orange, and back to red.

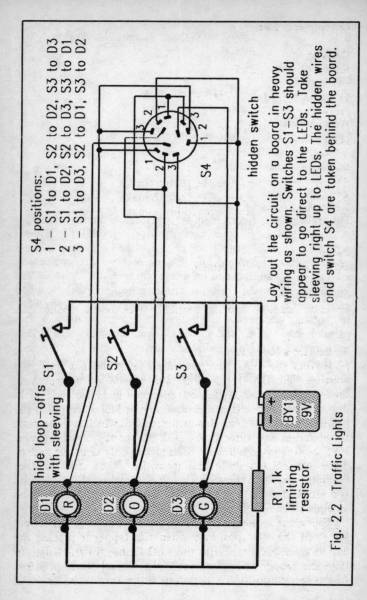

S4 positions:
1 – S1 to D1, S2 to D2, S3 to D3
2 – S1 to D2, S2 to D3, S3 to D1
3 – S1 to D3, S2 to D1, S3 to D2

hidden switch

Lay out the circuit on a board in heavy
wiring as shown. Switches S1–S3 should
appear to go direct to the LEDs. Take
sleeving right up to LEDs. The hidden wires
and switch S4 are taken behind the board.

S4

hide loop–offs
with sleeving   S1

S2

S3

BY1
9V

R1 1k
limiting
resistor

D1 (R) D2 (O) D3 (G)

Fig. 2.2 Traffic Lights

20

Components Lists

Resistor
R1   1kΩ

Light-emitting diodes
D1   red
D2   orange
D3   green

Switches
S1   single-pole, push-to-make
S2   single-pole, push-to-make
S3   single-pole, push-to-make
S4   3-pole, 3-way rotary

Battery
BY1   9V with clip

Miscellaneous
Panel or shallow box if necessary (see text), wiring, etc.

3. Inspect a Morse Key

Show that the Morse key, mounted on a box has only two controls: an ON/OFF switch and the Morse tapper key. Switch on and you can tap out messages in Morse code without any problem If a spectator knows Morse, so much the better. If not, you can demonstrate SOS, which is three dots, three dashes and three dots. Ask him to tap out a message. He'll be frustrated when he finds he can only send out dashes. Take it back and show him it works. Give it to another spectator and he'll think he's going dotty when all he can send is a series of dots. Tell them they'll need to get together in an emergency to send out an SOS.

The secret is the 3-way rotary switch hidden in the tapper key. In the first position, when the tapper is pressed the circuit gives out a tone and the LED flashes for the length of time the tapper makes contact — the normal Morse position. In the second position, the output is present for the length of

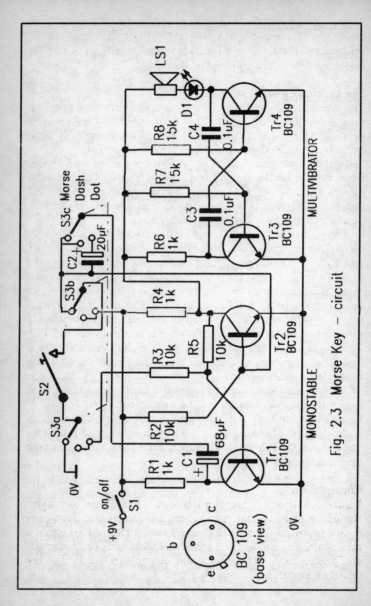

Fig. 2.3 Morse Key – circuit

22

a dash, no matter how long the tapper is held down, or how many taps are made during that 'dash' period. In the third position, the output is present for the length of a dot no matter how long the tapper is held down.

The Circuit (Figure 2.3)
The basic audio oscillator circuit is a multivibrator formed by transistors Tr3 and Tr4. The frequency of oscillation is determined by C3, C4 and R7, R8. The sound and light outputs are derived from the collector circuit of Tr4.

In the Morse position of S3 (shown), it can be seen that a 0V is applied via the Morse key S2 to the base of Tr2. This 0V effectively cuts off Tr2 as each Morse character is sent, and supplies positive pulses from the +9V rail, via R4, of a corresponding length to power the multivibrator.

Transistors Tr1 and Tr2 form a monostable circuit. As its name implies, this circuit has only one stable state — Tr1 off and Tr2 on. Transistor Tr2 is held on by resistor R2 tied to the +9V rail. The output from Tr2 collector is therefore zero.

In the Dash and Dot modes, operating the Morse key S2 connects Tr1 base via R3 and the key to the +9V rail. Transistor Tr1 switches on and the right-hand plate of capacitor C1 drops to a minus voltage momentarily and switches off Tr2. This is the unstable state, and Tr2 goes high for a short period until the capacitor recharges via R2. The circuit then returns to its stable state.

In the Dash position of S3, only the 68μF capacitance C1 is in circuit and the duration of the unstable state ($0.7 \times$ R2 $\times$ C1) gives an output pulse of almost half a second (a dash).

In the Dot position of S3, C1 is connected in series with a 20μF capacitor C2, which reduces the duration of the unstable state to give a short dot.

Construction
Figure 2.4 shows a suggested layout. The Morse key knob should be plain so that it is not obvious that it also doubles as a rotary control for S3. The tapper switch (S2) can be either a microswitch as shown, or a set of make contacts located under the plastic strip. The only other control on the box is the ON/OFF switch S1.

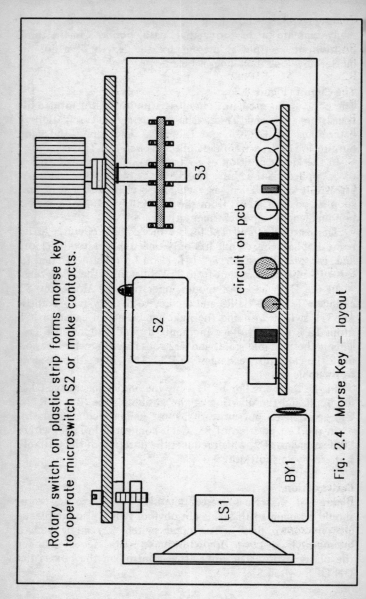

Rotary switch on plastic strip forms morse key to operate microswitch S2 or make contacts.

S3

circuit on pcb

S2

BY1

LS1

Fig. 2.4 Morse Key – layout

24

Components List

Resistors
R1	1kΩ
R2	10kΩ
R3	10kΩ
R4	1kΩ
R5	10kΩ
R6	1kΩ
R7	15kΩ
R8	15kΩ

Capacitors
C1	68μF 10V
C2	20μF 10V
C3	0.1μF plastic foil
C4	0.1μF plastic foil

Semiconductors
Tr1	BC109
Tr2	BC109
Tr3	BC109
Tr4	BC109
D1	TIL209

Switches
S1	S.P.S.T.
S2	S.P.S.T. microswitch (see text)
S3	3-pole, 3-way rotary

Loudspeaker
LS1	64 ohms

Battery
BY1	9-volt with clip (PP3)

Miscellaneous
Suitable box, stripboard and connecting wire.

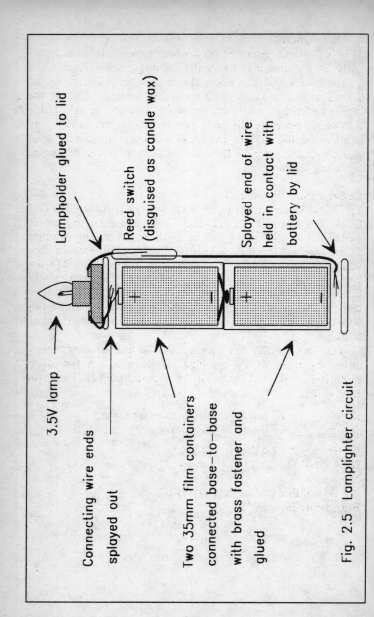

3.5V lamp

Connecting wire ends splayed out

Two 35mm film containers connected base-to-base with brass fastener and glued

Lampholder glued to lid

Reed switch (disguised as candle wax)

Splayed end of wire held in contact with battery by lid

Fig. 2.5 Lamplighter circuit

26

4. Lamplighter

This is a simple electrical trick where a candle-lamp is apparently lit by bringing the light of a magic wand close to it.

The candle houses a series circuit of a lamp, a battery and a reed switch. As the magic wand is brought close to the candle to light it, a magnet, mounted close to the light inside the wand, operates the reed switch. Grip the candle, and another magnet held in the hand will keep the candle lit as you remove the wand. Blow on the light, to put it out as you move the magnet away.

Construction (Figure 2.5)

The candle can be made up with whatever materials are to hand. For example, an old torch could be used with the reed switch taking the place of the push switch. The example shown was made up from two plastic 35mm film containers, which fortunately are just right for housing an R14-size battery. A brass paper-fastener through the bases of the containers provides electrical contact between the batteries, and the lids provide sufficient pressure to hold the connecting wire ends in contact with the extreme ends of the two batteries.

The reed switch can be disguised as drip of candle wax, either by paint or by applying candle wax. A few other imitation drips will help divert attention away from the reed switch.

Components List

Lamp — 3.5V m.e.s.
Batteries — 2 × 1.5V
Reed relay
Magnet
2 × 35mm film containers (white)
Brass paper-fastener.

Chapter 3

LIGHT FANTASTIC

Here are some light demonstrations that Edison never dreamed of when he developed the electric light bulb.

1. What Power Cut?

This trick is similar to the 'Open Circuit' trick in Chapter 1, but requires no sleight of hand; another circuit that refuses to go open even when you cut it!

Show a string of low-voltage lamps connected in series and plug it across a battery. Unscrew each of the bulbs in turn to demonstrate that if you have an open-circuit in a series circuit, all the lamps will go out.

Grasp a chosen section of the cable between two bulbs and cut it, or ask a member of the audience to cut it, with a pair of wirecutters. To the surprise of the audience, the lamps remain on. Continue to hold the two cut ends together for a moment to give the impression that you may be concealing a join. Then hold the ends apart for all to see.

The trick lies in the wiring up of the circuit as shown in Figure 3.1. What looks like single-core linking cable is in fact thin two-core or braided cable. The lamps are connected in series in the two halves of the chain. The extra core of the cable is used to connect the two remote lamps (LP2 and LP3, the ones separated when the cable is cut) via a link across the battery connections.

Preparation

The number of lamps in your series circuit will depend on their voltage and the voltage of the battery. For example, you could have four 2.5V or three 3.5V MES bulbs in series across a 9-volt battery. The explanatory diagram Figure 3.1 shows four lamps in circuit. Bulb-holders of LP1 and LP2 should be wired in series using one core of the cable. The other side of LP1 should be wired, using the same core, to the inner connection of the red phono plug, PL1. The other core of the cable runs continuously from the right-hand side

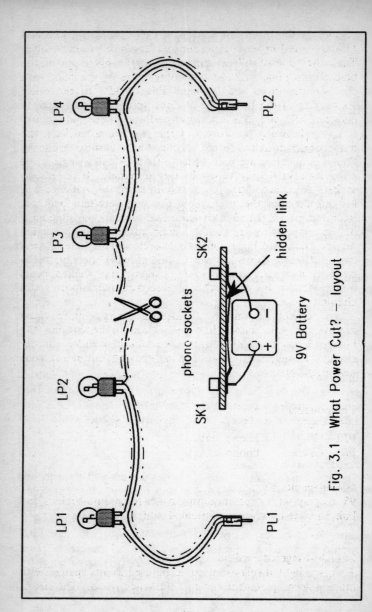

Fig. 3.1 What Power Cut? — layout

of LP2 to the outer connection of PL1. Similarly, LP3 and LP4 are wired in series using another length of two-core cable. The other side of LP4 is connected to the inner pin of the blue phono plug, PL2, and the other core of the cable runs continuously from the left-hand side of LP3 to the outer connection of the PL2. The obvious link cable wired directly between LP2 and LP3 is really superfluous. The hidden link is a wire between the outers of the two phono sockets, the inners of which are connected via clips to the battery terminals. Phono connectors are used because they look like single-point plugs connected only to the battery terminals. If the phono sockets are spaced apart on a paxolin strip, the audience will not suspect that the vital connection lies between them. It is important to the trick that the two separate dangling ends of the lamp string are seen! I must confess that although I set the trick and knew what to expect, when I first saw the two separated halves of the circuit glowing merrily, for a moment it seemed unbelievable. Maybe this trick appears more effective for those who have been brought up on series circuits!

The circuit diagram of Figure 3.2 offers a more visual explanation. It shows that the section to be cut has the hidden loop in parallel, which provides continuity for the circuit. Remember to renew the link that was cut before your next performance.

Components List

LP1 — LP4	2.5V m.e.s. lamps with holders
PL1 — PL2	Phono plugs
SK1 — SK2	Phono sockets

Miscellaneous
9V battery with clips, mounting panel for phono sockets and link, insulated, two-core or braided cable (see text).

2. Light-Fingered Freddie
This is a light display that could be used as an 'opener' with musical accompaniment and in a darkened room. The circuit

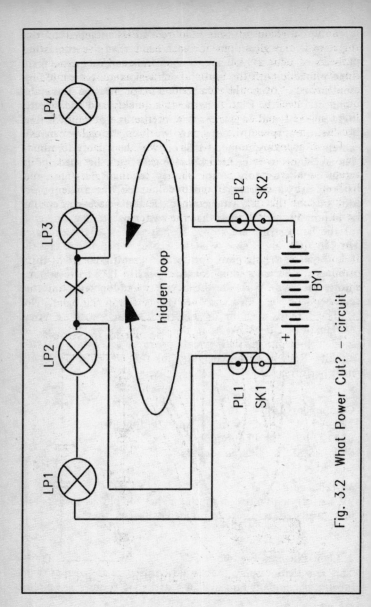

Fig. 3.2 What Power Cut? – circuit

is simply a chain of four coloured LEDs attached to the finger ends of a glove, one for each hand, that give interesting patterns of light as you move your arms and/or spread your fingers in time with the music — an ideal exercise for budding conductors! You could even write a magic message in the air, but you'll need to learn to write this quickly and backwards. Four fingers together give a more intense line of light for fine brush strokes; spread the fingers to work on a broader 'canvas'.

For a changing colour pattern, two ideas came to mind. Two different colour LEDs per finger could be used in an astable multivibrator circuit similar to that given for the harbour lights. Easier still, one bi-colour LED per finger could be used and the only other circuit elements necessary would be a miniature switch to reverse the battery.

The Circuit

If you go for the simplest option, the circuit consists of four ordinary LEDs connected in series with a PP3 battery. As shown in Figure 3.3, the LEDs are wired or sewn on the finger-end of the glove and the battery fits in the palm. No

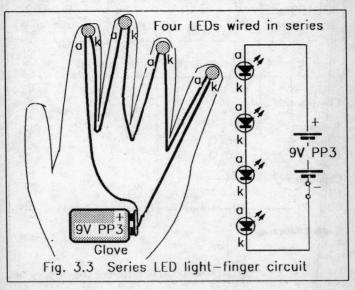

Fig. 3.3 Series LED light–finger circuit

switch is required as the battery clip can be disconnected after the act.

If you want an automatic colour change every few seconds, use two different colour LEDs per finger, i.e. one from the D1 – D4 chain and one from the D5 – D8 chain. A suitable astable circuit is shown in Figure 3.4. The change-over time depends on the values of C1, R1, and C2, R2. Reduce these values if a quicker change-over time is preferred, and vice versa.

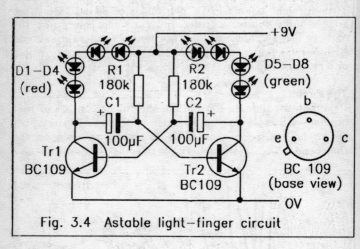

Fig. 3.4 Astable light—finger circuit

Components List

Resistors

R1	180kΩ
R2	180kΩ

Capacitors

C1	10 – 100µF (see text)
C2	10 – 100µF (see text)

Semiconductors

Tr1	BC109
Tr2	BC109
D1 – D8	D1–D4 & D5–D8 different colour patterns.

34

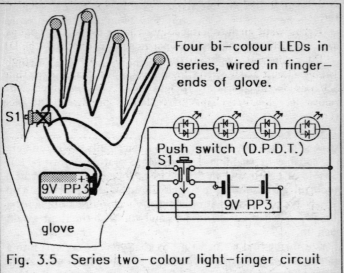

Four bi—colour LEDs in series, wired in finger—ends of glove.

Push switch (D.P.D.T.)
S1

9V PP3

glove

Fig. 3.5 Series two—colour light—finger circuit

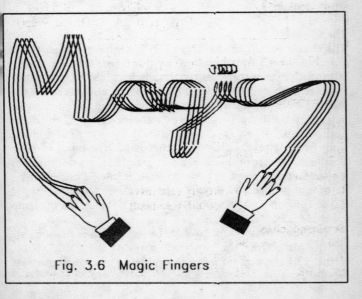

Fig. 3.6 Magic Fingers

35

A straightforward mechanical switching circuit (Figure 3.5) can be made by connecting four bi-colour LEDs in series and using a miniature double-pole, double-throw switch to change over the battery polarity. The miniature push switch or slider switch can be operated by the thumb. Space writing with changing colour patterns will really give the impression that you have magic fingers (Figure 3.6).

3. Magic Lamp

An Aladdin's lamp, talisman of Arabian Nights, unfortunately not capable of enabling the holder to gratify any wish, but capable of lighting when touched or rubbed. This could be a colourful and useful prop to include in your apparatus. You can always rub it, say 'Abracadabra' when you're looking for a miracle, or when a trick misfires and you wish the floor would open up.

You might find a small tin box that you can convert into a lamp, but remember that you need to keep the metal handle isolated from the body of the lamp, as these provide the two touch contacts.

The Circuit

The circuit for the lamp (Figure 3.7) is a Schmitt trigger touch switch followed by a transistor output stage. The input gate IC1a of the Schmitt trigger is normally held low by resistor R1 connected to the 0V line. The input is also taken to the metallic body of a decorative Aladdin's lamp. The metallic handle of the lamp (isolated from the body) is taken to the positive rail. When the handle is held by one hand and the lamp body is touched by the other hand, the input of IC1a goes high. Inversion takes place in gate IC1a, its output goes low and so the input to inverter IC1b is low. Consequently, its output is high and provides the necessary base current via R3 to turn on Tr1. So while the touch contacts on the lamp are made, LP1 lights.

A further refinement would be to insert a monostable circuit, made from the two spare gates of the CMOS 4011, so that LP1 stays on for a few seconds after the touch contacts are made.

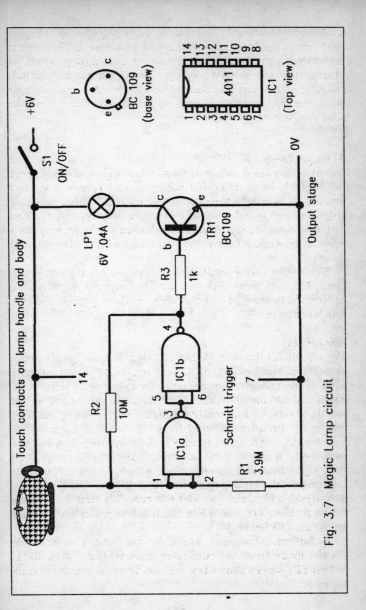

Fig. 3.7 Magic Lamp circuit

37

Components List

Resistors
R1   3.9MΩ
R2   10MΩ
R3   1kΩ

Semiconductors
IC1   4011
Tr1   BC109

Switch
S1   S.P.S.T.

Lamp
LP1   6V 0.04A

Miscellaneous
Material for lamp shape. This should house components and provide two isolated metal contacts for touch control. 6V battery and connectors, 0.1-inch stripboard and connecting wire.

4. Lights Out or Lights On?

Here's a circuit that can be quite puzzling. Ask someone to switch on the light and it comes on before the light switch is reached. Similarly, if the light is on, it will go out as your hand or a fluffy cotton-wool cloud gets near to the switch. The circuit could fit inside a doll's house or cardboard model house with the light shining through the window, controlled by an exterior switch — and a hidden sensing device!

The secret sensor is a light-dependent resistor (LDR) placed near the switch, activated by the amount of light falling on it. A hand approaching the switch shades the LDR, which increases its resistance and causes the transistor to change state.

The switch itself provides an extra facility. It converts the circuit to act as either a light-operated switch, or a dark-operated switch giving the opposite effect.

The Circuit (Figure 3.8)

The circuit is simply a light-dependent resistor (LDR) controlling a transistor switch. The slight complication is the double change-over switch which is used to make two circuits out of one.

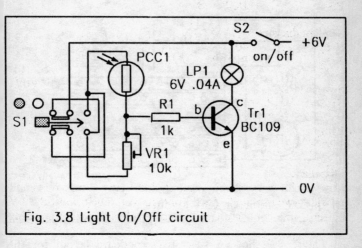

Fig. 3.8 Light On/Off circuit

Dark gives light

With S1 in the position shown in the figure, the LDR (PCC1) is connected between the base and 0V line and the variable resistor VR1 is between the base and the positive rail. This is the dark switch-on position of S1. When light falls on PCC1 its resistance is very low. This means that the available base current is low and Tr1 is turned off, so lamp LP1 is off. If PCC1 is now covered, its resistance increases and base current flows to transistor Tr1 via VR1 and R1. The transistor turns on, collector current flows and LP1 lights.

Light gives light

If S1 is switched to the other position, PCC1 is now connected between the base and the positive rail, and VR1 is connected from the base to 0V. This is the light switch-on position of S1. Covering PCC1 increases its resistance, reduces the base current and holds off Tr1 and LP1. Exposing

PCC1 to light reduces its resistance, provides base current to turn on Tr1 and the lamp.

Adjustment of the variable resistance VR1 controls the point at which base current will flow or cease to flow.

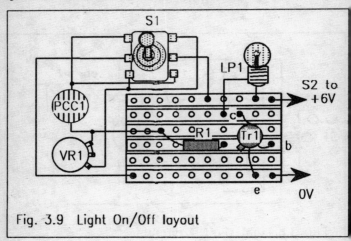

Fig. 3.9 Light On/Off layout

Figure 3.9 shows a suggested stripboard layout for this circuit. However, as there are only two components mounted on the stripboard, it could be replaced by a tag-strip. The few components can be mounted on a small panel or wherever convenient for the particular application.

Components List

Resistor
R1   1kΩ
VR1   10kΩ log. carbon

Switches
S1   D.P.D.T. (toggle or slider)
S2   S.P.S.T.

Semiconductors
PCC1   ORP12
Tr1   BC109

Lamp
LP1   6V 0.04A m.e.s. bulb

Miscellaneous
Model house, 6V battery and clips, connecting wire.

5. Manpower

Lighting up electric light bulbs with your bare hands can be quite spectacular and there are several ways of creating this illusion. Perhaps the simplest way is to use an ordinary frosted light bulb. First offer this around the audience to show that it is the genuine article. You then pass this from your left to the right hand, hold it in the palm of the hand and mysteriously it appears to glow. The source of light is a low-voltage bulb hidden in the palm of your hand behind the mains bulb and connected to a battery (see Figure 3.10). The frost effect on the mains bulb diffuses the small light source and gives the impression that the bigger bulb is lit. A variation on this trick is to conceal a small lamp in a finger-stall (or glove-finger). It is then quite easy to hold the frosted mains bulb in the hand with the finger-stall light behind it.

Another manpower effect, to light low-voltage bulbs held in the hand, is to wear a glove or a flesh-coloured thumb- or finger-stall with two contacts sewn into it, leading to a hidden battery and switch. The contact wires must be the correct distance apart to bridge the bulb contacts. A little careful rehearsal will be needed to make this effective.

Yet another impressive trick can be performed with a frosted mains lamp that has come cleanly away from its base. **To avoid a nasty cut, don't try removing one**, and I'm not suggesting that you have high-voltages up your sleeve! Solder a small low-voltage lamp inside the base, across the contacts, and glue it back on to the bulb portion. You now have a large size low-voltage lamp to play tricks with, but when not in use, keep it in your box of tricks well away from mains circuits. Take a look at the two-contact glove idea shown in Figure 4.8 for the battery connections. Do not use heavy-duty batteries in case you short-circuit the contacts!

41

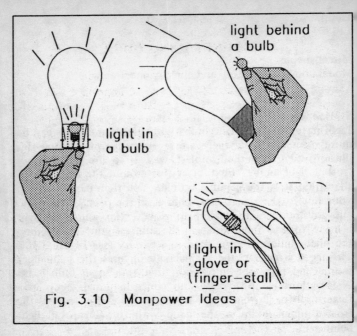

Fig. 3.10 Manpower Ideas

Using very fine gauge wires, you can make one or more of these low-voltage bulbs move in space without any visible means of support.

Parts List
Various size light bulbs, gloves or finger-stall, flashlight battery supply as outlined in the text.

Important Note
Never be tempted to try any sorts of tricks with mains or high voltage bulbs or equipment. It could be most dangerous!

Chapter 4

SOUNDS INCREDIBLE

Sound is the end result of radio and an important part of the
output of television. It is not surprising, therefore, that
sound has a chapter in a book about magical electronics. If
sound is the effect on ears caused by vibrations, have you
ever thought that a giant tree crashes *silently* to the ground
in a forest if there are no ears to hear it. It sounds incredible!

1. Ringing the Changes

Several imitation handbells are placed on a table. Pick them
up one by one and shake them to show that only one of them
rings. Change them around and ask a spectator to point out
the handbell that rang. Surprisingly, the spectator will guess
wrong each time. Ring the bell again and ask the audience to
watch carefully as you proceed to shuffle them slowly. No
matter how carefully they watch, they will never choose the
one that rings. Finally, get the spectator to upturn the handbells one by one to show they are empty. For good measure,
you might let the bell circuit you have concealed, perhaps up
your sleeve or in some innocent-looking object on the table,
ring again as you put each bell away. This trick can be most
appealing!

The secret is to press the small pushbutton switch concealed in your hand whenever you want the hidden bell circuit to
ring. As you will be holding a handbell somewhere near at
the same time, the sound will seem to be coming from it as
you give it a shake.

Preparation

Effective imitation handbells are easily constructed from some
everyday articles from your local DIY centre: half a dozen
plastic flowerpots, a length of plastic overflow piping and a
tin of gold lacquer or car-spray. The handle is formed by a
5-in length of plastic piping glued into a hole in the base of
the flowerpot. This joint can be strengthened by first cutting
and splaying out the end of the piping before inserting it.

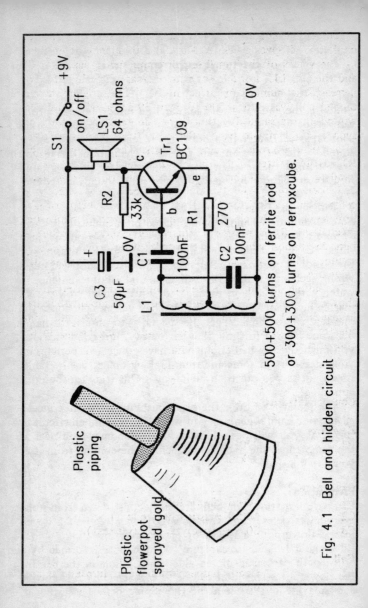

Fig. 4.1 Bell and hidden circuit

44

The circuit (Figure 4.1) is a transistor version of a Hartley oscillator. It gives a bell-like note at a frequency determined by the values of the tuned circuit components, capacitor C2 and the coil L1. For a lower note, increase the value of C2 or increase the number of turns on L1. The original centre-tapped coil was 300 + 300 turns of 39 s.w.g. wire scramble-wound in the same direction on a 1-in ferroxcube core. If such a core is not to hand, 500 + 500 turns on a short piece of aerial ferrite rod gives similar results. The tapping-point via R1 to the emitter of Tr1 means that the two halves of the winding are in anti-phase, the correct condition for feedback and oscillation. The tap does not need to be exactly at centre-point. Resistor R2 from base to collector of Tr1 provides bias. The electrolytic capacitor C3 charges up when pushbutton S1 is pressed. This charge voltage briefly sustains oscillation when S1 is released, giving a bell-like decay sound. The decay time can be extended by increasing the value of C3.

A simple layout for the bell circuit using stripboard is shown in Figure 4.2. As space is allowed to mount the small loudspeaker LS1 on the stripboard, there is adequate room for the few other components without using breaks in the copper strips.

Components List

Resistors
R1   270Ω
R2   33kΩ

Capacitors
C1   100nF plastic foil
C2   100nF plastic foil (see text)
C3   50μF electrolytic 10V (see text)

Coil
L1   Centre-tapped winding on ferroxcube core or ferrite rod (see text)

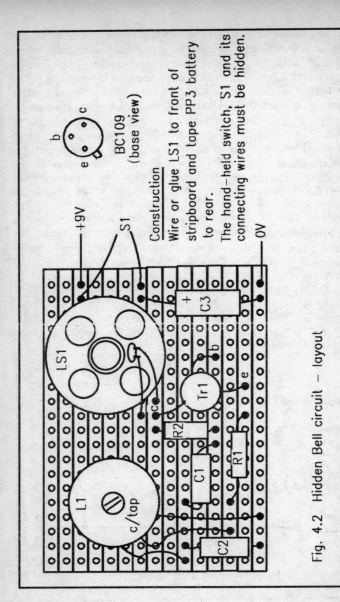

Fig. 4.2 Hidden Bell circuit – layout

BC109
(base view)

Construction

Wire or glue LS1 to front of
stripboard and tape PP3 battery
to rear.

The hand-held switch, S1 and its
connecting wires must be hidden.

46

Loudspeaker

LS1   64 ohms miniature or electro-magnetic
                   earpiece

Switch

S1   S.P.S.T. pushbutton

Semiconductors

Tr1   BC109

Miscellaneous

Handbell materials as described in text, 9V PP3 battery,
stripboard and wire, etc.

2. Playing by Ear

Quite a few musicians can 'play by ear', but when they do it
literally, it's magic if not musical!

This circuit produces sounds at frequencies dependent on
the skin resistance between VR1 and the +9V rail. The two
transistors Tr1, Tr2 and associated components, shown in
Figure 4.3, form a simple astable multivibrator oscillator
circuit. In effect, it is two amplifier stages that are cross-

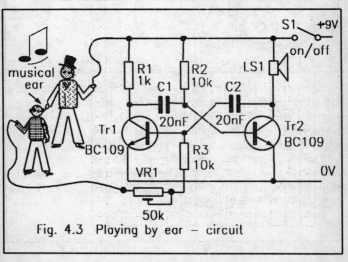

Fig. 4.3 Playing by ear – circuit

47

coupled. The necessary feedback for oscillation is obtained by connecting the collector of Tr2 via C2 to the base of Tr1. The frequency-determining components are C1, R2 and C2, R3, VR1 and the skin resistance in series. Reduce the values of C1 and C2 to increase the frequency, and vice versa. The two flying leads are best terminated in metallic rods or plates to ensure a good hand grip with minimum resistance. Try it yourself first.

A suggested stripboard layout is shown in Figure 4.4.

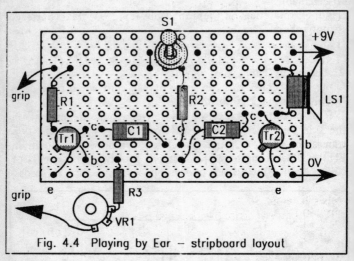

Fig. 4.4 Playing by Ear — stripboard layout

This trick can be set up by first touching the flying lead end grips together. You can then play a little tune by varying potentiometer VR1, while switching S1 on and off to provide the rhythm. Ask if anyone can play by ear or has a good 'musical ear'. Hand the +9V grip to your volunteer, take hold of the other grip and switch on. You now touch his or her ear with your free hand to see how musical it is. Clammy hands give best results. Like writing, this trick is literally 10% inspiration and 90% perspiration.

Components List

Resistors

R1	1kΩ
R2	10kΩ
R3	10kΩ
VR1	50kΩ potentiometer

Capacitors

C1	20nF plastic foil
C2	20nF plastic foil

Loudspeaker

LS1	64 ohm loudspeaker, or 3—8 ohms with output transformer

Switch

S1	S.P.S.T.

Semiconductors

Tr1	BC109
Tr2	BC109

Miscellaneous

PP3 9V battery, stripboard and wire, etc.

3. Baffling Bass

This is not really a trick, but is such an impressive demonstration of the properties of sound waves that it sounds like magic. The method is shown in Figure 4.5. When a hinged baffle board is brought up to a free-standing loudspeaker, the treble sound of the music is transformed into one that gives plenty of rich bass tone. The reason for this improvement in bass response is that the baffle prevents low frequencies at the front and rear of the loudspeaker cone from cancelling out. As the high frequency waveforms are more concentrated, they are not so affected. The hinged baffle can be either lifted into place by hand, or better still, wound up by a pulley cable attached to the board. You

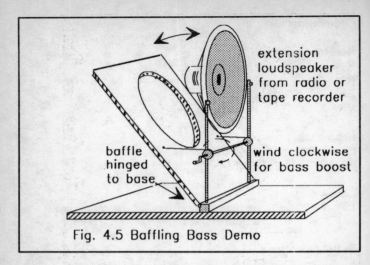

Fig. 4.5 Baffling Bass Demo

could describe this as a mechanical bass control. The speaker can be fed from the loudspeaker sockets of a radio or a tape recorder with the internal speaker muted.

An excellent pushbutton-operated demonstration of this effect was given as part of the audio display in 'Evoluon', the Philips permanent electronics exhibition hall at Eindhoven in the Netherlands.

4. Bird Calls

This is another sound effect that is produced by a simple oscillator circuit. The broad title 'Bird Calls' was used because although the prototype circuit sounded like a seagull, the Mark II version sounded more like a duck, and the final was a very good imitation of a cockerel in full cry at first light. When the pushbutton S2 is pressed there is a chirp from the speaker, which continues at intervals for a few moments after S2 is released.

The Circuit (Figure 4.6)

The function of Tr1 is to enable the audio oscillator circuit of Tr2. When pressed, switch S2 supplies base current via R1 to

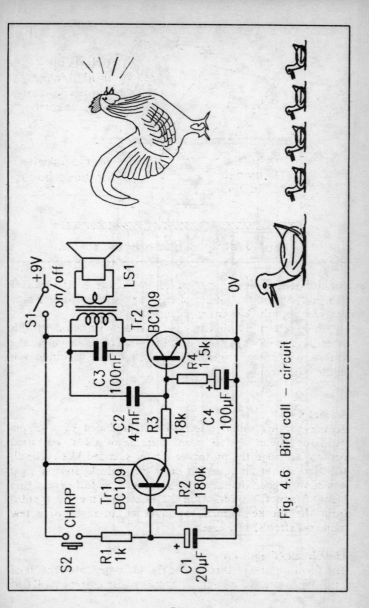

Fig. 4.6 Bird call — circuit

51

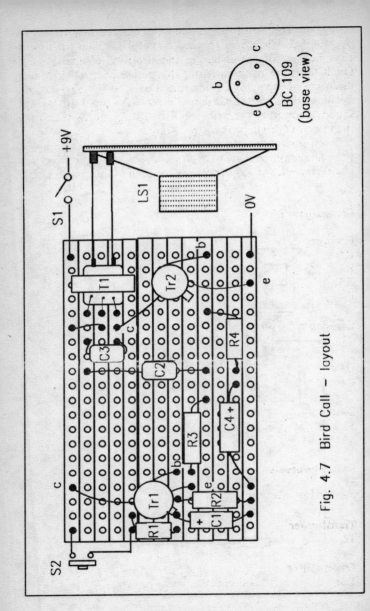

Fig. 4.7 Bird Call – layout

switch on Tr1, which in turn supplies base current via R3 to operate Tr2. When S2 is released, Tr1 still conducts for a short time because of the charge in the electrolytic capacitor C1. Oscillations are maintained for this period by the charge and discharge of capacitor C2 connected back to the base of Tr2. Smaller values of this capacitor increase the pitch of the bird sound. Lowering the value of R4 slightly and/or increasing the value of C1 will prolong the agony.

A stripboard layout for this circuit is given in Figure 4.7. For simplicity, this constructional layout closely follows the circuit layout, and no breaks are required in the copper strips.

Components List

Resistors
R1	1kΩ
R2	180kΩ
R3	18kΩ
R4	1.5kΩ

Capacitors
C1	20µF 10V
C2	47nF plastic foil
C3	100nF plastic foil
C4	100µF 10V

Switches
S1	S.P.S.T.
S2	S.P.S.T. push-to-make

Semiconductors
Tr1	BC109
Tr2	BC109

Transformer
T1	output (tapped primary)

Loudspeaker
LS1	3—8 ohms

5. Wire-Less Wonders

"Why did they call it wireless when it's a mass of wires," people used to say, looking into the back of a wir.., a radio, a transistor set, you say as you disentangle a speaker from a jumble of wires and components in a cabinet that looks like an antique radio. If you have an old radio, or a bird's-nest of a circuit that looks like one, put it there to misdirect the audience. It will make them think that it's the source of the sound you are about to produce.

Using the two contact glove method (Figure 4.8), also illustrated in the 'Manpower' trick in Chapter 3, you can coax music out of the hand-held loudspeaker, apparently wire-less. The finger contacts resting on the two speaker connections supply the audio output via two thin wires up your sleeve leading away to the extension loudspeaker sockets of a hidden transistor radio. The internal speaker must of course be disconnected. The hand-held idea shown in Figure 4.8 is one method, but with a little ingenuity the loudspeaker contacts

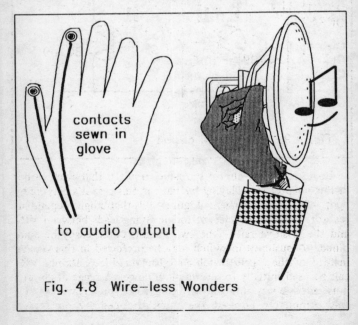

contacts sewn in glove

to audio output

Fig. 4.8 Wire-less Wonders

can be arranged to mate with audio output contacts on a Close-up Mat (see Chapter 6) or even a chair. The old party game 'Musical chairs' could have a whole new meaning if a chair is wired for sound.

6. Light Music

Wave a hand between the light and a light-dependent resistor and this circuit will produce some unusual musical sounds. With a little stretch of the imagination, we could call this light music.

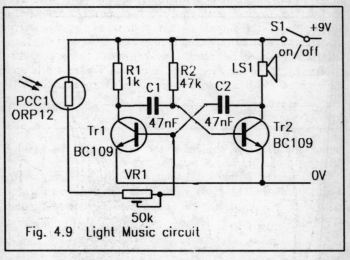

Fig. 4.9 Light Music circuit

For this, we use almost the same circuit as that given earlier in this chapter for 'Playing by Ear'; in this case it's playing by light. The main change in Figure 4.9 is that a light-dependent resistor, PCC1, is connected to the flying leads between VR1 and the positive rail — the two circuits could easily be combined. A pushbutton switch may be preferred in this version instead of the toggle switch S1. The variable resistance VR1 can be used initially to set the pitch range. A range of about a musical scale was obtained with the prototype, i.e. when PCC1 was completely covered the pitch dropped by an octave.

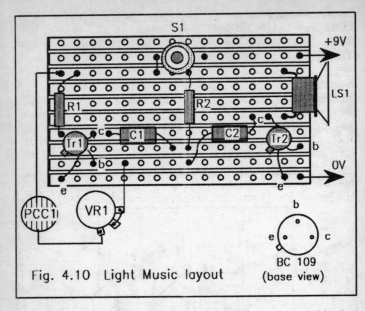

Fig. 4.10 Light Music layout

Some unusual spine-chilling sound effects are possible by waving the hand from side to side.

A suggested stripboard layout is shown in Figure 4.10. The light-dependent resistor PCC1 is not mounted on the board as its location will depend on your particular application.

Components List

Resistors

R1   1kΩ
R2   47kΩ
VR1   50kΩ carbon

Capacitors

C1   47nF
C2   47nF

56

Semiconductors

PCC1	ORP12
Tr1	BC109
Tr2	BC109

Switch

S1	S.P.S.T. toggle or push-to-make

Loudspeaker

LS1	miniature type 64 ohms or magnetic earpiece

Miscellaneous

9V battery (PP3) with clip, stripboard and wiring.

Chapter 5

MIND BOGGLING

Here is some magic of the mind. If you are not very good at sleight-of-hand you could include one or two of these mind-bending tricks in your programme.

1. Safe Cracking

A safe combination lock has been tampered with by an intruder. There are four interlock control plunger keys, three of them detonators. Your task is to guide a member of the audience through a safe unlocking procedure from a remote position. Meanwhile, tension mounts as a red warning light flashes and the detonator circuits tick away ominously.

Four control plunger keys are available for the interlocks. Three are marked 'detonator' and the other is marked 'pass'. These are all inserted by the spectator in any of four sockets that lie horizontally in a row across the safe control panel between you and the spectator. It is important that you note the position of the 'pass' key by a quick glance. All you need to remember is whether it was in an odd or even position counting from the spectator's left (your right). Tell him to concentrate on the 'pass' key while you turn your back on him and try to read his thoughts. You will then ask him to switch the 'pass' key with one on its right or left, whichever one he chooses. Of course you won't know which one, you add, and if the 'pass' key is at the end of the row, it must be switched with the one that is next to it. Every time you say 'switch' he must switch the 'pass' key with one of the adjacent keys as before. You say 'switch' five times in all, but don't make this obvious.

So far, the procedure is standard wherever the 'pass' key was first inserted in the row of four.

At this stage mention that you can have no idea where the 'pass' key is but the spectator must concentrate on it.

Actually, if the 'pass' key was inserted in an even position (2 or 4) from the spectator's left, then by simple maths, after five moves it will now be in an odd position (1 or 3).

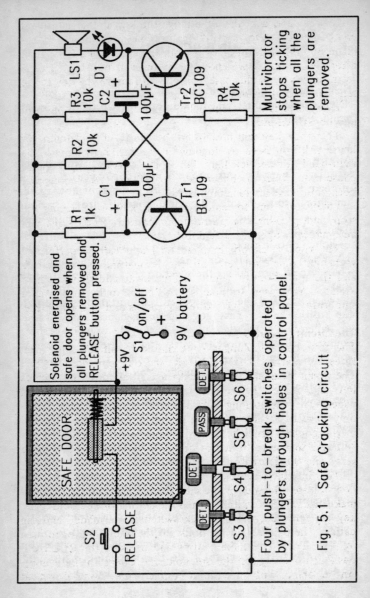

Fig. 5.1 Safe Cracking circuit

Multivibrator stops ticking when all the plungers are removed.

R3 10k
LS1
D1
C2 100µF
Tr2 BC109
R4 10k

R2 10k

R1 1k
C1 100µF
Tr1 BC109

Solenoid energised and safe door opens when all plungers removed and RELEASE button pressed.

+9V
S1 on/off
9V battery
+
−

SAFE DOOR

S2
RELEASE

DET. DET. PASS DET.
S3 S4 S5 S6

Four push-to-break switches operated by plungers through holes in control panel.

In this case, ask him to remove the key at the right-hand end of his row. However, if the 'pass' key was initially inserted in an odd position (1 or 3 from the spectator's left), then after five moves it will now be in an even position (2 or 4 from his left). In this case, ask him to remove the key at the left-hand end of his row.

Everything is now plain sailing again. Ask him to perform another switch-over.

The 'pass' key will now be in the centre of two detonator keys. All you need to do now is to ask him to remove the right-hand key and left-hand key in turn. You must of course pause in between to concentrate, to make it less obvious that both outer keys are being removed.

Finally, ask him to remove the 'pass' key — the ticking will stop and pressing the pushbutton marked 'RELEASE' will automatically open the safe door!

The trick is simply mathematical and can be performed with four coins, cards, etc., but the detonators, the locked safe and the multivibrator circuit ticking away add that touch of drama. You need to practise this trick to be sure it goes smoothly; try it out with three 2p pieces and one 10p piece.

The Circuit (Figure 5.1)
The four control plunger keys should be all the same size; three are marked 'DETONATOR' and one is marked 'PASS'. These can be metal blocks with a central foot that locates into any one of the four socket holes drilled in the control panel. There is nothing magical about the control keys. They only have to actuate the four push-to-break switches located in the control panel holes (so should be heavy enough). It will add that extra touch of drama if the pass key is painted green and the detonator keys are red for danger.

The interlock switches are connected in series with the door-release solenoid for the safe, the battery, and the push-to-make 'RELEASE' switch. When the detonator keys and 'pass' key are removed, the interlock switches are 'made', and the path to the 0V line via R4 holds off the multivibrator formed by Tr1, Tr2. The ticking stops and pressing the RELEASE pushbutton energises the solenoid and opens the safe door. An old relay, with or without contacts, may be used instead

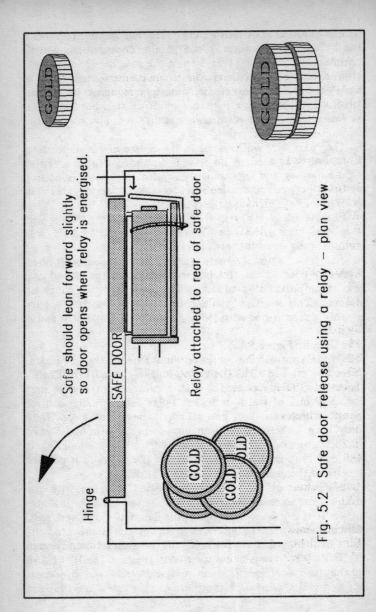

Safe should lean forward slightly so door opens when relay is energised.

Hinge

SAFE DOOR

Relay attached to rear of safe door

Fig. 5.2 Safe door release using a relay – plan view

of a solenoid as shown in Figure 5.2. You will need a rubber band for the armature release if the contacts have been removed.

The timing components for the multivibrator are R2, C1, and R3, C2. The speed of the tick can be regulated by varying these values; increase values to slow down the speed and vice versa.

Components List

Resistors
R1	1kΩ
R2	10kΩ
R3	10kΩ
R4	10kΩ

Capacitors
C1	100μF, 10V
C2	100μF, 10V

Switches
S1	S.P.S.T.
S2	S.P.S.T. push-to-make
S3 – S6	S.P.S.T. push-to-break

Solenoid or relay (see text)

Semiconductors
Tr1	BC109
Tr2	BC109
D1	LED

Loudspeaker
LS1	64 ohms

Miscellaneous
Box with hinged door for safe, control panel, four plungers, 9V battery with clip, connecting wire.

2. Take it as Red

This is a very simple prediction trick. Beforehand, you have concealed a glowing red necklace under a top hat.

You tell the audience that you are investigating the theft of a necklace. You do not know what colour it is, but if the audience will co-operate, you will try to restore it to its rightful owner.

You then ask the spectators to call out names of colours, which you appear to write down on separate slips of paper. These slips are folded and dropped into a box. Draw attention to the top hat by saying that you don't know where the necklace is, but the thief may have given away a vital clue when he was heard to say to an accomplice "keep this under your hat!". Then ask a spectator to draw out a colour from the box. The colour will be red (because you wrote red on all the slips, and red is sure to be called out, particularly if you use an accomplice). With a flourish, lift up the top hat and the glowing red necklace under it will confirm your prediction.

The necklace circuit is four red LEDs in series across a 9-volt PP3 battery. This circuit is the same as that used for the Magic Bracelet in Chapter 1.

3. Six of the Best

A board with cut-out spots forming the shape of a six is illuminated from the back initially by a rotating disc. The spectator must think of a number above five and when your back is turned, start counting to himself from the tail of the six, pointing to the spots in turn. When he arrives at the number he thought of, he starts counting again in the reverse direction around the circle, and makes a mental note of the spot he stops on. You then turn and slowly rotate the disc to illuminate the spot on which he stopped. The trick is mathematical, the spot always being the same irrespective of the number chosen. To distract attention from this, the board can be turned through 90 degrees for a second attempt to show another six with a different number of spots in the tail so that the end of count occurs on some other spot. Naturally, you must remember where this is.

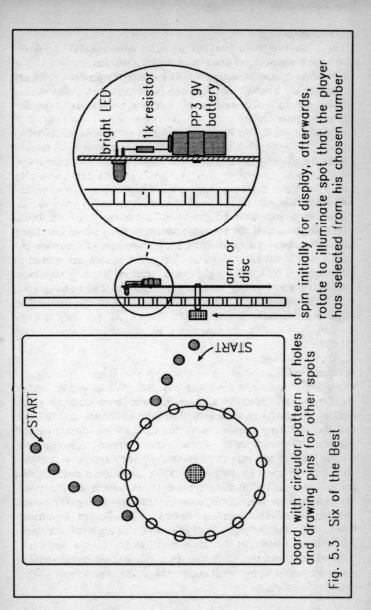

board with circular pattern of holes
and drawing pins for other spots

bright LED

1k resistor

PP3 9V battery

arm or disc

spin initially for display, afterwards,
rotate to illuminate spot that the player
has selected from his chosen number

START

START

Fig. 5.3 Six of the Best

Construction

The apparatus for this is simple to arrange. Basically all you need is a number of spots on a board, but the rotating arm or disc with a light attached makes it more attractive. A suggested layout is given in Figure 5.3. Fourteen equally-spaced holes are drilled in a circular pattern as shown, and coloured drawing pins can be used for the two tails that form the start. The LED circuit is attached to an arm (or disc) slightly larger than the circle of holes at the rear of the board. A spindle fixed to the centre is rotated by a control knob on the front.

4. Into Thin Air

Take an object with a light affixed, e.g. one of the Harbour Lights, and tap it on the table to show that it is solid. Drop this into the top cup of a stack of several plastic cups on the table. Pick up an empty paper bag and hold it open in your left hand. With your right hand, remove the top cup from the stack and transfer it slowly to your left hand and drop it into the paper bag. Then screw the bag and the plastic cup into a small ball and toss it into the air. If this trick is done smoothly, it will seem that the solid object has vanished into thin air.

Preparation

You will need to remove the base of the top plastic cup so that when you lift it out, the solid object remains in the stack out of sight of the audience. Make sure that the plastic cups are sufficiently opaque so that the light on the object cannot be seen when it is in the stack. As you transfer the top cup, tilt it slightly towards the audience so they cannot see that it has no base. As a further ploy to convince them that the object is still in the cup, fix a light in a finger-stall (or in a glove) so they see a little glow in the top of the cup as you transfer it across to the paper bag. A small light circuit can be devised using two button cells and a 3mm LED similar to the circuit used in the Hanky Panky trick in Chapter 1. During the transfer, this can be switched on by a pressure contact operated as you grip the side of the cup.

Parts List

Solid object, e.g. Harbour Light or other chunky object with a battery-operated LED on top.

Stack of two or three plastic or paper cups.

Glove or flesh-coloured finger-stall.

Two button cells, 3mm LED, pressure contact and wire.

5. Indian Rope Trick

All over the mystic east there are many versions of this world-famous trick. Rewards have been offered for anyone who can perform this illusion in the open air. Here is a successful miniature version that can be most rewarding in the field of light entertainment.

Preparation

Solder a super-bright red LED to about 9-in of twin fine wire — the rope! The trick works well with either very flexible multi-strand insulated wire or 32 s.w.g. enamelled wire. The principle is very simple as can be seen from Figure 5.4. A strong magnet is placed about half-an-inch above the LED, with the bottom end of the 'rope' attached to a base. The rope rotates slightly with movement but remains attracted to the magnet. You can say that the red light on top is a modern innovation to warn low flying aircraft.

Note that some LEDs are not attractive! No, there's nothing wrong with their appearance, but they don't have ferrous leads. If your LED doesn't respond to the magnet, slip a suitable steel washer over the top of the domed part and glue it to the rim. Another solution is to tape a small magnet to the dome of the LED. To maintain the correct distance between the LED and the magnet, the trick can be housed in a clear plastic tube, the kind used for storing rolled-up documents, etc. If one is not available, a suitable tube can be made by rolling up and gluing an A4-size sheet of plastic. The diameter depends on the size of two plastic lids (search the kitchen for coffee jars) used for the ends. Attach the strong magnet to one and a PP3 battery and a 680-ohm series resistor to the other. When the best distance has been

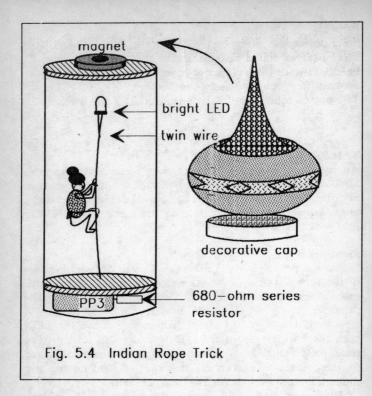

Fig. 5.4 Indian Rope Trick

found for the 'rope', secure it to the base with adhesive tape. Since legend has it that a small boy climbs up the rope you can model him from expanded polystyrene, paint him and glue him on. You might say that the bright lad is after the bright LED. Finally, decorate the tube and add an attractive cover to make it look like a minaret.

Presentation
Start the trick with the rope lying on the base. You can say that as the trick originated in the sub-continent you must try it with the rope the other way up. Invert the tube, and once the LED is near to the strong magnet is should remain there when you turn the tube the right way up.

Parts List
Bright LED, PP3 battery, 680-ohm limiting resistor, strong magnet, fine wire, and suitable materials for housing the trick.

Chapter 6

TRICKS OF THE TRADE

Finally, here are some magician's tricks of the trade suitably electrified to brighten up your performance.

1. A Magic Wand

As well as being the recognised symbol of power, the magic wand can be a useful device for helping with your tricks.

Our magic wand is a ten-inch length of three-quarter inch, translucent white tube, described in the DIY stores in more down-to-earth terms as overflow pipe. This is perhaps a little tubbier than we need, so if you can say the magic word when you visit your DIY store and find a smaller diameter pipe, so much the better; the battery sizes are the determining factor. You will also need to find or make two end-stoppers; these can be of cork, plastic or wood dowel.

Construction (Figure 6.1)

Like most things, you get out of it what you put into it. So here's what you put into it: a lamp at one end, wired in series with a reed switch and two AA-size batteries, with a magnet at the other end.

And we get light out of it when a magnet is brought close to the reed switch. The magnet can be either hand-held, secreted in another magic wand, or in the Magnetic Close-up Mat described later. Another attractive idea is to strip the case off an old 1.5V battery and use it as a cover to disguise a magnet. What's more, the empty battery case without its ends has potential for another trick. It can also be hand-held and used to produce your magic wand, and a never-ending stream of other things, from up your sleeve.

Two identical wands could be made with a magnet and lamp at one end and a reed switch at the other end. These wands would both light when reversed and held together. Alternatively, one wand could have the magnet and lamp at one end, and the other wand have the reed switch and lamp at one end. In this way, you could light one wand from a hand-

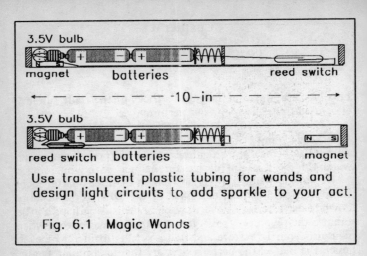

Fig. 6.1 Magic Wands

Use translucent plastic tubing for wands and design light circuits to add sparkle to your act.

held magnet and then use the light from this wand, apparently to light the other.

No doubt your magic wand will produce other ideas. The wands can be decorated if you are artistic, and a string of LEDs inside a wand could also brighten up your act.

Parts List

Plastic tubing (translucent); 10-in length with stoppers.

Reed switch.

Magnet.

3.5V m.e.s. lamp.

3V battery (two AA-size batteries, or AAA-size depending on tube used).

Connecting wire, etc.

2. Magician's Top Hat

Traditionally you'll need a top hat and unless you've got an old one that you can mutilate, Figure 6.2 shows how to make one out of cardboard. Several ideas can be used to add some sparkle, but as the hat will be used for covering other things as well as your head, any decoration is best confined to the top section. For illumination, a number of LEDs can be spaced

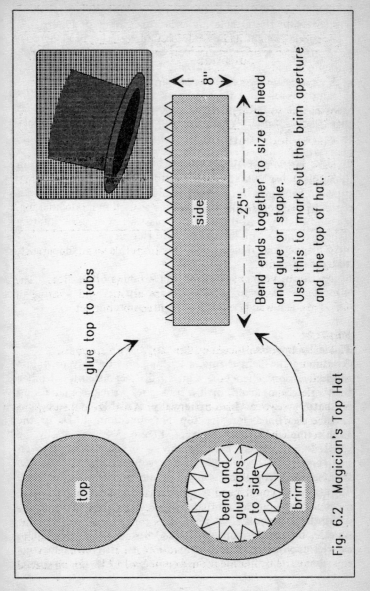

glue top to tabs

top

bend and glue tabs to side

brim

side

← 8" →

- - 25" - -

Bend ends together to size of head and glue or staple.
Use this to mark out the brim aperture and the top of hat.

Fig. 6.2 Magician's Top Hat

73

around the crown, for instance, two strings of four flashing alternately in the astable multivibrator circuit of Figure 3.4.

A sound-to-light circuit idea could also be used here to good effect. A microphone concealed in the hat could pick up sounds and cause the LEDs to twinkle on and off. Many such circuits are given in the popular magazines.

Simpler still, if circuit-building is not your forte, LEDs are available in red, green and yellow from *Maplin Electronics* that flash at about twice a second when a supply voltage range between 3.5V and 13V is applied. No series resistor is necessary within this supply voltage. Each LED has a forward current of about 9mA at 9V, so several can be run in parallel from a 9V (PP6) battery.

Movement may be preferred to light, and if a slow-speed motor is available, a low-voltage type as used in model-making, it could be fitted to drive a small plastic fan or some rotating ribbons to make you look like a Mad Hatter.

Materials
Sheets of cardboard: 25-in × 8-in for side of hat
                        7-in × 8-in for top
                        12-in × 11-in for brim

3. Flashy Bow-tie
Continuing the light theme, a flashing bow-tie may provide a good diversion when you want to distract attention from a tricky sleight of hand, or if a trick goes wrong. Such a kind of natty neck-wear is commercially available, but the light circuits described for the top hat, bi-colour LEDs or the astable multivibrator circuit of Figure 3.4 may easily be adapted to fit on an existing bow-tie or on any comic over-size version that you make up for your wardrobe. You can always house the circuit in an inside pocket of your coat.

4. Magnetic Close-up Mat
As a focus point, many magicians use a close-up mat. This can be much more than it seems to be to assist in performing electronic tricks. Some ideas are suggested in this magnetic

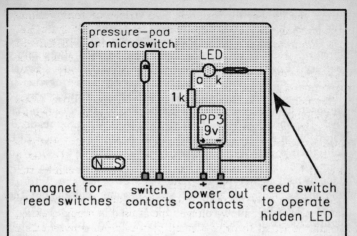

Suggested layout with components embedded in expanded polystyrene under translucent surface.

Fig. 6.3 Magnetic Close-up Mat

version and in the Conductive Close-up Mat that follows. For instance, the two mats could be combined, and many other ideas will no doubt spring to mind. Depending on your programme, a mat, or several, can be adapted to suit your special tricks. As shown in Figure 6.3, a mat can conceal a magnet for operating a reed relay in a magic wand or in some container that you put on the mat. It can also conceal a voltage supply with a reed switch in series to energise a device on the mat when desired. For instance, a lamp or a buzzer resting on the mat, and bridging two hidden contacts, can be operated by placing a magnet, concealed in a wand or in the casing of an old battery, on the mat near to the reed relay.

A further possibility is a mat with a white surface, that hides a coloured LED, or several, in a circuit embedded in the mat. This circuit can be lit at a certain time, for example, to give the impression that the light is coming from a device in or under a semi-translucent tumbler or plastic cup placed over the LED(s).

You will no doubt think of several uses for this embedded circuit. Here is one using the magnet inside the dummy battery. For this trick you will need to embed the reed switch and LED of the series circuit of Figure 6.3 close together in the close-up mat. Say that you have found a quick way to connect up circuits. Place a plastic cup on the close-up mat over the spot where the reed switch and LED are embedded. Drop in an LED of the same colour as your embedded LED and then a few short lengths of wire. Finally, drop your dummy battery containing the magnet. This will actuate the hidden reed switch and the embedded LED will glow through the plastic cup. As you lift away the cup and tip out the loose components, the hidden LED will go out. You can of course locate the reed switch away from the LED for other effects.

A variation on this trick is to use two tumblers and two light circuits, each operated by a hidden magnet in the other tumbler. The parts you will need will depend of course on the circuit or circuits you choose, but your conductive close-up mat can be an interesting project in which to incorporate some of your own ideas.

5. Conductive Close-up Mat

A close-up mat with disguised metallic strips, is a useful accessory. The strips can be alternately positive and negative to supply an LED for instance, or the extension speaker leads of a transistor radio. The mat is faced with a sheet of silver foil gift-wrapping paper, the kind that is non-conductive, to disguise the conductive silver strips that are glued over this to provide the supply rails (see Figure 6.4). These should run towards the magician so that there is easy access to the end connections. To prevent a direct short-circuit caused by placing metallic objects on the mat, a dropping resistor is connected in series with any battery supply. As suggested, for some tricks, the alternate strips could be output leads from a radio to operate a small loudspeaker placed on the mat. The spacing between strips

foil strips on non-conductive paper   expanded polystyrene tile

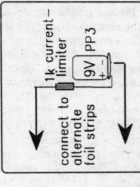

1k current–
limiter

connect to
alternate
foil strips

9V PP3
+ –

Suggested layout with components embedded in expanded polystyrene
covered with metallic foil strips. These can be used to light LEDs,
or to produce sound from a speaker by connecting an audio source
to alternate strips instead of the battery.

Fig. 6.4   Conductive Close-up Mat

must coincide with the spacing between contacts on the devices to be energised. The ON/OFF switch can be either a toggle switch on the magician's side of the mat or a suitably placed reed switch and magnet.

6. LED Balloons

Here is a colourful prop that can be included along with the Light-fingered Freddie display as it works better in dimmed lighting. Four super-bright LEDs (or eight in two chains) are connected in series and inserted into a white balloon which is then blown up. The two lead-out ends can either be connected directly to a 9-volt battery (see Figure 6.5) or perhaps included in a sound-operated switch circuit, operated by a microphone.

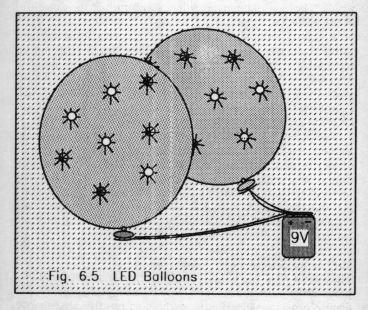

Fig. 6.5 LED Balloons

Another suggestion is that the LED display used for the Finale could be adapted with balloons. In its present form, however, it would present a challenge — rather like trying to build a ship in a bottle!

7. Finale

It is important to round off your performance positively with something spectacular. The audience has to know that it's the end, otherwise your performance will fall flat; so why not emulate the movies and show it in lights.

As you will realise, there are several ways of doing this in varying degrees of complexity. Perhaps the simplest method is to cut out the letters 'THE END' from a cardboard box, put a sheet of coloured celluloid over the holes and shine a light behind it. This requires little electrical skill so needs no further explanation. However, if your skills are in model-making you can let them run riot on this. For instance, the cardboard box could be designed to look like a TV screen, or you could design a giant telescope in cardboard with the words 'The End' illuminated when you turn it in the direction of the audience.

A slightly more sophisticated version, seeing there are two words, is to use two 6V bulbs to replace the LED strings in the astable circuit of Figure 3.4 and to replace the 9V battery with a 6V. Partition off the two words so that the two separated words flash on alternately at a speed governed by the circuit values. Use a different colour filter for each word, or letter, to make it more effective.

The *pièce de résistance* if you have an abundance of LEDs and are reasonably familiar with electronic circuits is a decade divider display as shown in Figure 6.6. The LEDs, four per output, are arranged in sequence on a card panel or on a flag to form the letters 'The End' (see Figure 6.7). This is truly *the end* in displays, with the words picked out in coloured, running lights with the added effect that they can be controlled in speed.

The Circuit (Figure 6.6)

The circuit used the ubiquitous 555 timer in astable mode to provide the pulse inputs for a decade timer IC2. The decade divider provides ten outputs, each going positive in sequence when pulses are applied from IC1. This means that four LEDs of the display switch on at a time to provide the running letters (D1 to D40) for the ten outputs. The display repeats continuously with the reset pin 15 connected to the 0V. The

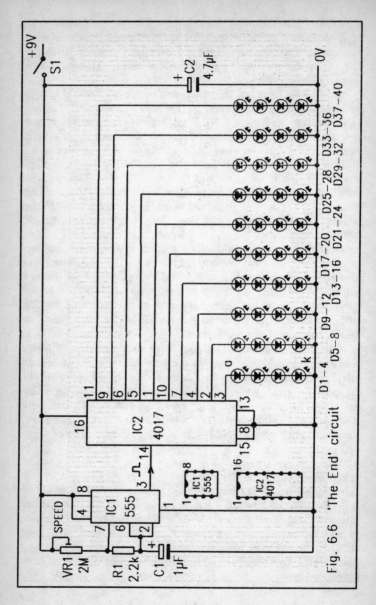

Fig. 6.6 'The End' circuit

80

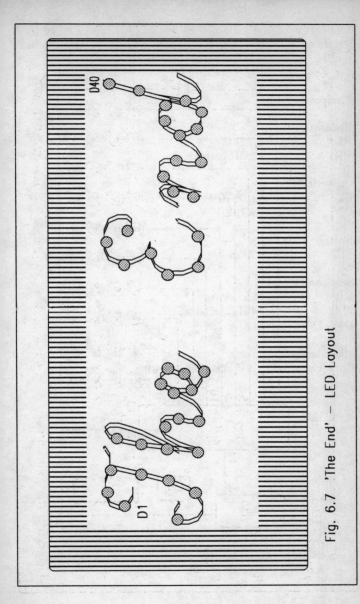

Fig. 6.7 'The End' — LED Layout

81

flashing speed is determined by the SPEED setting of control VR1 and can be varied during performance to give the best results.

Components List

Resistors
R1   2.2kΩ
VR1   2MΩ carbon

Capacitors
C1   1μF 10V
C2   4.7μF 10V

Switch
S1   S.P.S.T.

Semiconductors
IC1   555 timer
IC2   4017 decade divider
D1 – D40   LEDs

Miscellaneous
Circuit board, PP3 9V battery and wiring.

Figure Index

Figure		Page

Please note following is a list of other titles that are available in our range of Radio, Electronics and Computer books.

These should be available from all good Booksellers, Radio Component Dealers and Mail Order Companies.

However, should you experience difficulty in obtaining any title in your area, then please write directly to the Publisher enclosing payment to cover the cost of the book plus adequate postage.

If you would like a complete catalogue of our entire range of Radio, Electronics and Computer Books then please send a Stamped Addressed Envelope to:

BERNARD BABANI (publishing) LTD
THE GRAMPIANS
SHEPHERDS BUSH ROAD
LONDON W6 7NF
ENGLAND